Fox Fables

Contents

The Fox and the Stork

Fox invited Stork to dinner.
He couldn't wait to play a trick on her.

"I hope you like soup," said Fox,
as he placed her bowl on the table.

3

Fox sat down and lapped up his soup.
"Oh, this soup is very good," he said.
"Do you like it, Stork?"

Stork tapped her beak on the bowl.
The soup smelled so good that
it made Stork's stomach rumble.
But she couldn't get even a sip
of soup.

Stork didn't like Fox's trick.
Then she had an idea.

"I'm not very hungry, Fox,"
she said. "But will you come to my home
for dinner tomorrow?"

"I'd love to," said Fox.

When Fox arrived at Stork's house,
Stork put two vases filled with soup
on the table. She dipped her long beak
into one vase and sipped up the soup.
"This soup is wonderful," she said.

Fox's tongue couldn't reach
into the vase. He couldn't even
taste the soup. He knew Stork
had tricked him, too.

"Do you like the soup?" Stork asked.

Fox left with his head hanging down.

Moral

If you play a trick, you might be paid back.

7

The Fox and the Crow

Fox watched Crow fly by.
Crow had a piece of cheese in her mouth.

"Oh, how I love cheese," thought Fox.
"Crow won't give it to me,
but I know how to get it."

8

"Crow!" Fox called.
"You look very lovely today."

Crow stopped on a branch
to listen. She liked to hear
nice things about herself.

"Your eyes are so bright,
and your feathers shine
like the moon," said Fox.

Crow flapped her wings
to show off her feathers.

"I know your song is more beautiful
than your feathers. Will you sing
for me, Crow?" asked Fox.

Crow was so pleased
that she didn't stop to think.
She opened her beak and cawed.

Fox waited below with his mouth
wide open. He snapped up the cheese
and danced away.

Moral

Don't trust kind words from unkind people.

11

The Fox Who Couldn't Wait

Fox's belly growled. He was very hungry.

Then, inside a hole in a tree,
he saw a sack. He could smell it.

"A hunter must be storing his meat here,"
said Fox. "Lucky for me!"

He squeezed into the hole.
It was a tight fit.

Fox ate one piece of meat, and
then another, and then another.
Finally, he was full.

"I will save the rest for later,"
thought Fox, and he began to squeeze
out of the tree. It was a little tighter
than before.

Then Fox smelled the meat again.

"If I wait till later, I'll spend all my time
thinking about this delicious meat.
I better just eat it now," he decided.

When Fox was done,
his big, round belly hurt.
He tried to squeeze out of the tree.
But his aching belly was far too fat.

Just then, Crow came by.
She laughed. "Why Fox, it looks like
you're stuck! You'll just have to wait
till you're thin and hungry again," she said.

Days passed.
At last, Fox was just
as thin as before.
His hungry belly growled
as he slipped out
of the tree.

Moral

It is often
helpful to be
able to wait.